THIS BOOK BELONGS TO:

....

© AL-AQSA PUBLISHERS 2011
Reprint: 2021

Al-Aqsa Publishers
P.O. Box 5127
Leicester
LE2 0WU

E-mail: info@aqsa.org.uk | Website: www.aqsa.org.uk

Illustrated by Farah Khan

Design and Layout by Shoayb Adam

With special thanks to Sanam Mirza

The Prophets in Palestine

Prophet Dawud عليه السلام

4

This story is about Prophet Dawud ﷺ and his amazing life.

Dawud ﷺ was the father of Sulayman ﷺ and they were both prophets.

The story of Prophet Dawud ﷺ shows us the importance of Masjid al-Aqsa. It also shows how Allah ﷻ blessed Dawud ﷺ and provided him with great things.

Dawud ﷺ lived in Jerusalem for most of his life.

The land in Jerusalem has been blessed by Allah ﷻ for all human beings, animals and even plants.

7

In the story of Musa ﷺ we learn how the Banu Israel escaped from Egypt and wondered in the desert around Palestine. They did not go inside Jerusalem as they were afraid of the people living there.

Dawud ﷺ was with the people of Banu Israel. When he was still very young, he joined the army of the Banu Israel who were planning to fight the people of Jerusalem so that they could live there.

A very strong and tough group of people called the Philistine lived in Jerusalem. Most of the Banu Israel were scared and did not want to fight the Philistine.

In fact, when it came to the battle, there were only a few hundred soldiers on their side, and the Philistine army had thousands of soldiers!

11

When Dawud ﷺ and the rest of the soldiers saw the Philistine army, they prayed to Allah ﷻ to give them patience and courage.

The leader of the Philistine army was a very tall and strong man called Jalut (known as Goliath).

Everyone was scared when they saw how big Jalut was. He looked like a giant.

But Dawud ﷺ was very brave. He stepped forward and said, "I will fight Jalut!"

The leader of the army said, "You are too young."

Then he looked around and asked, "Will someone else fight Jalut?"

Again, Dawud عليه السلام bravely stepped forward and said, "I will fight Jalut!"

One more time, the leader of the army said, "No, you are too young. Will someone else fight Jalut?"

For the third time, Dawud عليه السلام stepped forward and said, "I will fight Jalut!"

Dawud عليه السلام was very courageous, and the leader finally agreed to let him fight Jalut.

When Jalut saw Dawud ﷺ coming towards him, he was very surprised and cried out, "I will not fight such a young and weak boy."

Dawud ﷺ did not listen. In his hand, he had a small slingshot and he carefully placed a stone in it, ready to fight. He remembered to pray to Allah ﷻ and ask for His help.

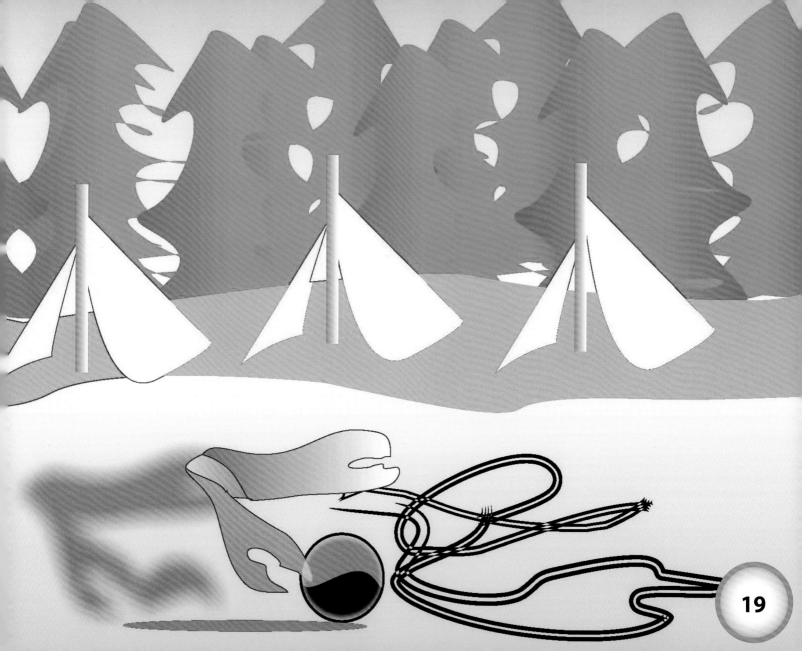

Jalut and Dawud ﷷ stood opposite one another.

Dawud ﷷ placed the stone he had in his slingshot and pulled it as far back as it would go, and quickly let go.

The stone went zooming through the air at incredible speed and hit Jalut on his forehead, right between his eyes.

Jalut fell down and hit the ground with a thunderous noise, and died.

Dawud ﷷ had beaten him!

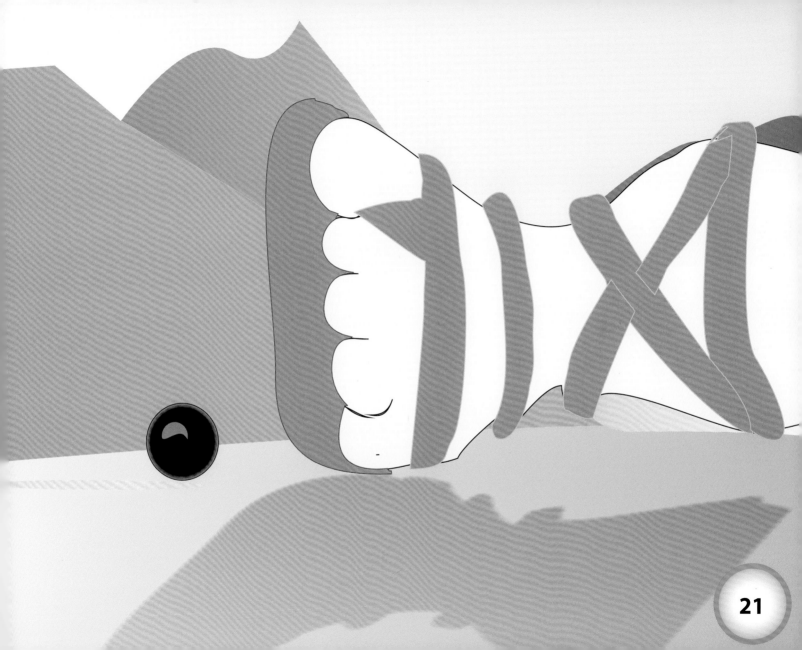

This was a great victory for Dawud عليه السلام and it was from Allah سبحانه وتعالى who had answered Dawud's عليه السلام dua.

The Banu Israel fought the Philistine army and they won, even though they had fewer soldiers on their side.

Dawud عليه السلام and his family and friends finally entered the blessed city of Jerusalem.

Years went by and Dawud عليه السلام grew older.

Then Allah ﷻ blessed him with something wonderful. He made Dawud عليه السلام the king of the people of Jerusalem and a prophet of Allah ﷻ.

Allah ﷻ only grants such an amazing favour to very special people.

Dawud  as a king and prophet in Jerusalem was sent special messages from Allah ﷻ.

These messages are called 'Revelations' and they were all put together in a book which was called the Zabur. In English we call it the Psalms.

Dawud ﷵ had a soft, beautiful and melodious voice which was given to him by Allah ﷻ.

When he used to recite the Zabur using this beautiful voice, all of the people, animals and birds used to gather around him, to listen and learn the words of Allah ﷻ.

The Qur'an says that even the mountains around Jerusalem used to praise Allah ﷻ with Dawud عليه السلام, each time he sang the praises of Allah ﷻ.

MashaAllah, what a blessed land it is!

Another special power that Allah ﷻ gave to Dawud عليه السلام was the ability to read very quickly. This meant that he could read the whole book of Zabur in less than a minute, even though it was over a hundred pages long.

Dawud عليه السلام had also been given great wisdom and was very clever.

When people argued or had disagreements, they came to Dawud عليه السلام and he had to judge wisely between them. This was a very big responsibility.

One day, when Dawud عليه السلام was praying in his private room on the land of Masjid al-Aqsa, two men suddenly appeared in front of him.

Dawud عليه السلام was surprised and a little bit worried when he saw them in his room.

The men told Dawud عليه السلام not to be afraid. They said that they were two brothers who had an argument, and they wanted his help to resolve it.

Dawud ﷺ agreed to help them.

They explained that one of the brothers had 99 sheep and the other brother only had one.

The brother with 99 sheep had taken the other brother's single sheep from him!

They wanted Dawud ﷺ to help them settle the dispute with justice.

Dawud ﷺ made his decision very quickly. He told the brother who had only one sheep:

"Your brother was wrong to take your sheep and add it to his flock."

He said that the sheep should be returned to its owner.

41

Both of the brothers then disappeared without another word.

Dawud عليه السلام then realised that the two men had been sent by Allah سبحانه وتعالى to test his judgement. Dawud عليه السلام was too quick when he made his decision and he should have listened to both of them before passing his judgement.

From this, we learn that we should always ensure that before making a judgement or decision, we listen to all sides of the dispute.

Dawud عليه السلام was very sorry for his mistake and he prayed to Allah سبحانه وتعالى for forgiveness.

Allah سبحانه وتعالى is very merciful and kind and so He forgave him.

This test from Allah سبحانه وتعالى taught Dawud عليه السلام how to be a fair judge and rule justly between the people in the land of Palestine.

Dawud ﷺ was blessed with another very special and amazing ability. When he held hard metal in his hands, it became soft and he could bend it any way he liked.

Dawud ﷺ was told by Allah ﷻ how to bend the metal to make special armour for the warriors to wear.

The armour was not heavy but it was very strong and flexible. This helped his army greatly as it protected his soldiers.

There was no other army in the world at that time who had the same armour as Dawud's عليه السلام soldiers. This was because Allah عزّوجلّ protected them.

Dawud ﷺ was the king of Jerusalem for 40 years. During this time, there was peace between the different tribes who lived in Palestine.

Towards the end of his life, Dawud ﷺ started to build Masjid al-Aqsa again.

The blessed Masjid was first built by Adam ﷺ after he built the Ka'bah in Makkah. After many years it lay in ruins and it was rebuilt by Prophet Ibrahim ﷺ. By the time Dawud ﷺ was the King of Jerusalem, Masjid al-Aqsa was again in ruins and this is why he started to re-build it.

The building of Masjid al-Aqsa was a big project.

Unfortunately, Dawud ﷺ died before the building was completed.

It was his son Sulayman ﷺ who continued the work and completed the building.

55

Prophet Dawud عليه السلام lived to the age of one-hundred. He was buried in Jerusalem but no one is sure exactly where.

However, there is a Masjid in Jerusalem called Masjid 'Nabi Dawud' which was built by the Ottomans to remind us of the great Prophet Dawud عليه السلام.

Dawud ﷺ lived a long life and he was blessed by Allah ﷻ. This is because he always remembered Allah ﷻ and prayed to Him for guidance and help.

There are many lessons which we can learn from this story, including how with the help of Allah ﷻ anything is possible!

Dawud عليه السلام was a very brave boy and he grew into a great man, king and prophet of Allah ﷻ. His life is a great example for us all.